Ella and Noah Celebrate Shabbat

Sticker Activity Book

Illustrated by Brenda M... Gracia and Gal Weizman
Designed by Michal Gil

יום ראשון: בריאת האור

It's nighttime and nocturnal animals are out and about. Can you name them?

How many sources of light can you spot?

Which one of these owls is sitting on the branch outside?

Draw stripes on my tail.

Trace and color in my wings.

Color me in.

Draw spikes on my back.

It's daytime and the nocturnal animals are sleeping.
Can you spot all five in the scene?

Color in the birds.
How many did you count?

Draw a line between the kids and their gear.

I want to play occer.

I want to ride a scooter.

Second creation day: the sky

יום שני: יצירת הרקיע

The sun makes rainbows when sunlight passes through raindrops.
Color in the rainbow and the sun.

Match the fish to the child.

Find seven differences.

Which of these boats is not like the others?

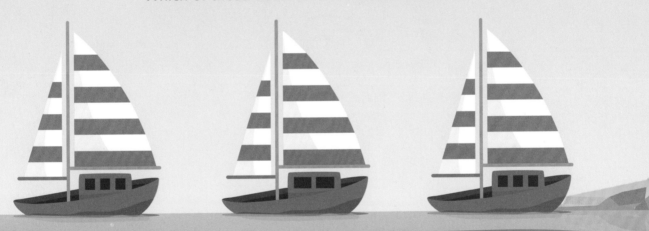

Which octopus and seahorse are not like the others?

Third creation day: land, seas and plants

יום שלישי: חשיפת היבשה, יצירת מקווה המים והצומח

Color in the beautiful flowers. Add some flowers of your own and color them in.

What a lovely vegetable garden! Spot fifteen differences.

Fourth creation day: Sun, Moon and stars

יום רביעי: בריאת המאורות

Match the astronauts and color them in.

Connect the dots, then color in the hidden picture.

Which of the three images is the boy seeing through his telescope?

Help the rocketship find its way to the blue planet.

Spot three satellites.

Spot four flying saucers.

Fifth creation day: birds and sea animals

Spot the bird carrying an olive branch.

There is only one fish in the ocean. Can you spot it?

Follow four easy steps to draw a bird sitting on a branch.

Follow four easy steps to draw a fish in the reef.

Sixth creation day: land animals and humans

יום השישי: בריאת חיות היבשה והאדם

The penguin, reindeer and fox all left footprints in the ice.
Can you match the footprints to the animals?

Which one of these arctic
animals has two babies?

Help Adam find his way to Eve.

Spot the snake in the scene.

After six days

At the end of the sixth day, creation is complete!

Have you seen Eve's hat?

Spot a yellow flower

Spot the bird with Adam's bag

A visit to the grocery store - Page 26-27

Cleaning the house -
Page 28-29

Cooking for Shabbat - Page 30-31

Getting Dressed for Shabbat - Page 32-33

Friday Night - Page 34-35

Shabbat dinner - Page 36-37

Visit the synagogue - Page 38-39

Havdalah -
Page 40

Creation days bonus stickers

Shabbat Word Search

W	C	A	N	D	L	E	S	F	X
T	S	D	C	H	A	L	L	A	H
O	E	W	R	E	S	T	L	M	A
R	K	I	D	D	U	S	H	I	V
A	O	N	Q	F	A	D	B	L	D
H	R	E	F	R	I	D	A	Y	A
J	E	S	H	A	B	B	A	T	L
S	Y	N	A	G	O	G	U	E	A
C	A	N	R	E	K	I	D	A	H
J	E	S	J	E	W	I	S	H	B

Word List:

- CANDLES
- JEWISH
- FAMILY
- FRIDAY
- HAVDALAH
- SHABBAT
- SYNAGOGUE
- TORAH
- WINE
- REST
- CHALLAH
- KIDDUSH

A Visit to the Grocery Store

Ella and Noah love grocery shopping for Shabbat. It's such fun to find the items on the shelves and add them to the shopping cart! They help to pick out all the ingredients needed for cooking their favorite Shabbat food.
Ella's favorite is homemade challah and Noah's favorite is kugel. What's your favorite?

Add Ella and Noah to this fun shopping scene
and fill their shopping cart with tasty ingredients.

Cleaning up for Shabbat

Shabbat is almost here, it's time to clean up! Help the family tidy up the house by sticking the tidy items on top of the messy ones.

Ella and Noah can't find these toys. Can you spot them in the room?

Cooking for Shabbat

Every Friday, Ella and Noah help their parents cook and bake for Shabbat. Their favorite part is helping out with the challah: Noah kneads the dough and Ella brushes the dough with egg wash and sprinkles with sesame seeds.

Use the stickers to fill the table with the ingredients and utensils needed for baking challah.

Getting Dressed for Shabbat

Shabbat is almost here and it's time to get washed and dressed.

Color in the shower curtain.

Use the stickers to fill the room with soapy bubbles.

Use the stickers to dress the family for Shabbat.

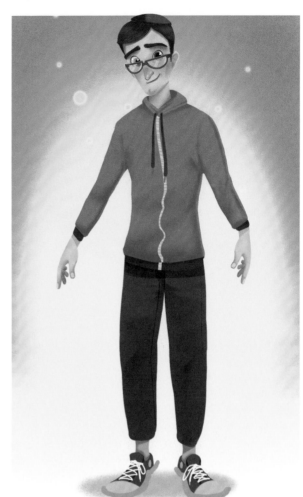

Friday Night

Add the missing items you will need for the Friday night Shabbat rituals: candlesticks with candles, wine, a two-handled cup and challah.

Lighting candles הדלקת נרות

Candles are lit before sunset. It is customary to give some coins to charity before lighting the Shabbat candles.

Kiddush קידוש

Kiddush is a blessing said over a cup of wine on Friday night. The cup is placed in the palm of the right hand when reciting the Kiddush.

Before we eat a meal with bread, we wash our hands and make a special blessing. A special cup with two handles is filled with water and poured over each hand.

The covered challahs are lifted and Hamotzi blessing is recited. Then the challah is cut, dipped in salt and eaten.

Shabbat Dinner

On Friday night, family and friends get together to celebrate Shabbat. Ella and Noah love singing Shabbat songs and listening to stories, but their favorite are the Shabbat riddles! Help them answer these tricky riddles.

Draw and fill the Shabbat table with food, wine, plates, flowers, silverware and more.

I'm a tasty braided bread, eat me plain or with a spread. What am I?

Fill me with wine
on a Friday night,
hold me up high
as Kiddush you recite.
What am I?

I have two big handles, I'm shaped like a cup,
fill me with water but don't drink me up.
What am I?

Place me
in the candlestick,
just before sunset,
light my wick.
What am I?

Visiting the Synagogue

Each week, Jews around the world visit the synagogue on Saturday morning to observe Shabbat. During the service, the Torah is taken out from the ark and the weekly Torah portion (parashah) is read. After the Torah has been read the scrolls are carefully put away again. If you're lucky, the service includes a Bar Mitzvah and you'll have a chance to collect the candy that is thrown from the pews.

Invite friends and family to the Shabbat morning service.

Havdalah הבדלה

On Saturday night, when three stars are twinkling in the sky, Shabbat comes to a close with the Havdalah ceremony. Havdalah is the ceremony marking the end of Shabbat and involves blessings of thanks over wine, spices, and a braided candle. Add the missing items you will need for the Havdalah ceremony: wine, Havdalah candle, Siddur, Kiddush cup and spice box.

Ella and Noah have placed their favorite Havdalah spices on the tray.
Can you name them?